Retold by Kathryn Smith
Illustrated by Stuart Trotter
Religious consultant: Meryl Doney
Language consultant: Betty Root

This is a Parragon Publishing book
First published in 2004

Parragon Publishing
Queen Street House
4 Queen Street
BATH BA1 1HE, UK

Printed in Indonesia

STORIES FROM THE BIBLE

Joseph's Coat of many Colors

p

Jacob had twelve sons, and he loved them all.
He loved Reuben, the eldest. He loved Benjamin,
the baby. And he loved each one in between.
But Jacob had a favorite—and that was Joseph.

One day, Jacob gave Joseph a new striped coat.

The coat had red stripes ...
green stripes ...
purple stripes, too ...
It had stripes like a
rainbow in every shade
and hue.

The other brothers felt jealous.
"We do all the work, and he gets
all the presents!" they complained.
It didn't help matters when Joseph
told them about his dream.

"I dreamed your bundles of wheat bowed down to mine!" he said. "Then the sun, the moon, and eleven stars bowed to me, too."

"What a big head you have!" cried Benjamin.

"What a show off!" grumbled the others.

"You and your dreams!" said Reuben. "Don't think WE are going to bow down to YOU, little brother!"

But Joseph couldn't help wondering if God was trying to tell him something important in his dreams.

One day, Jacob sent Joseph to find his brothers, who were looking after the goats in the fields far away.

So Joseph set off to look for them. The brothers spotted Joseph's rainbow coat a long way off.

"Look!" they cried. "Here comes Joseph in his striped coat. Let's give him what he really deserves."

RIP!   BUMP!

They tore Joseph's coat from him and threw him into a pit.

"HELP *!*" cried Joseph.
"Let me out of here!"

But his brothers wouldn't listen. They were too busy plotting how to get rid of him.

"We should kill him," they said. "Then we'll never have to see him or his coat again."

But Reuben shook his head. "Let's sell him to slave traders," he suggested. "We can dip his coat in goats' blood, then show it to Father. He'll think Joseph was killed by wild animals."

Soon some slave traders came by on their way to Egypt. The brothers sold Joseph for twenty pieces of silver.

Then the brothers returned home to show the blood-stained coat to their father.

Jacob was heartbroken when he saw it. But the brothers were still too full of anger and jealousy to feel sorry for what they had done.

"Let's see if Joseph's dreams come true now!" they jeered.

In Egypt, Joseph was sold to a very important man called Potiphar.

"I might never see my father again," thought Joseph, as his new master led him away.

Joseph felt scared. Joseph felt alone. But then he remembered his dreams, and that God was with him.

"I will work as hard as I can," he decided. "I will please God and Potiphar."

And that's exactly what he did.

He fetched and carried.
He worked and worked.
He NEVER grumbled.
He never shirked.
He worked as hard as any slave can ...
till Potiphar made him his right-hand man!

Potiphar was pleased with his new slave, but his wife was not! She wanted Joseph to do all sorts of wicked things, but he refused.

To get back at him, she lied about him, and had him thrown into prison.

But God was with Joseph in that deep, dark dungeon. And He had big plans for Joseph.

One day, a prisoner told Joseph about a dream he'd had the night before.

"I had a vine with
three branches," he said.
"Then I made wine for
Pharaoh, our king. What
can it mean?"
Joseph listened to the dream.
Then God told Joseph
what it meant.
"In three days you will be set
free, and serve wine to
Pharaoh," Joseph explained.
And that's just
what happened.

After that, everyone asked
Joseph about their dreams.
And God always helped him
explain them.

Before long, Joseph the
dream-teller became famous.
So famous that even Pharaoh
asked for his help.

"I dreamed seven skinny cows gobbled up seven fat cows," Pharaoh told Joseph. "What does it mean?"

"It is a message from God," said Joseph. "For seven years there will be lots of food. Then for seven years there will be none."

"We'll starve!" cried Pharaoh. "What should we do?"

"Save up food for the next seven years," said Joseph wisely. "Then there will be enough to eat when the famine comes."

Pharaoh was so happy, he set Joseph free.
"Joseph is my right-hand man," he announced.
"He is in charge of my food supplies. Everyone must
do as he says."

What did Joseph do then? He got to work, of course.

He filled up bags with grain.

He filled up barns with bags.

And he filled up the land with barns ...

till there was enough grain stored to feed all the people in Egypt, and more!

After seven years there was a famine, just as God had said. But Joseph had saved plenty of food to share.

Hungry people with rumbling tummies came from far and wide, looking for something to eat.

Even Joseph's brothers came.

"May we please have some grain?" asked the brothers.
They didn't recognize Joseph. But Joseph recognized them.

Joseph longed to hug his brothers. But he had to be sure that their hearts were no longer full of anger and hatred. So he played a trick on them. He hid a silver cup in Benjamin's bag. Then he gave each brother a big sack of food.

As the brothers turned to leave, Joseph cried, "Guards, search these men!"
Of course, the guards soon found the silver cup.
"Your brother is a thief!" cried Joseph. "He must stay here as my slave."

The other brothers fell to their knees and bowed down before Joseph. "Take one of us instead," they begged. "Benjamin is our father's favorite. He has already lost one favorite son. Please don't take another. It would break his heart."

At once, Joseph knew his brothers had changed. "Don't you know me?" he cried. "I'm your brother!"
The brothers all looked up and gasped. "Your dream about the wheat sheaves came true," they said. "We bow down before you!"

"This was all God's plan," said Joseph, hugging them. "He sent me to Egypt so I could help my family. Bring our father here too, so we can all live together again."

And that's exactly what they did.